Silent Flowers

SILENT FLOWERS

A Collection of Japanese Haiku

Edited by Dorothy Price

Illustrated by Nanae Ito

 Hallmark Editions

 Selected from "Haiku," Volumes 1-4, by R.H.Blyth, Hokuseido Press, Tokyo, Japan.
Printed in the United States of America.
Library of Congress Catalog Number: 67-17899

Introduction

Wordsworth defined poetry as "emotion recollected in tranquillity." Japanese haiku fulfill that definition with significance and beauty. They represent a whole world, a manner of daily living, and a religious and poetic experience. Masters at recognizing a certain "something" in unexpected situations, haiku poets recreate small moments discovered in the real world but suggesting the world of the spirit.

The three best-known haiku poets — Basho, Buson and Issa — wrote during the 17th and 18th centuries. Basho (1644-1694) was a religious man, a poet who found God in nature. Buson (1715-1783), an artist, dealt with existing things in their concrete immediacy — the here and now. Issa (1763-1827) was a humanist, concerned with man, birds and beasts in their struggle for survival.

Traditionally about nature, most haiku include a seasonal reference — a hazy moon always means spring; a cold moon indicates winter; "flowers" are usually cherry blossoms. But the season itself is not necessarily the real subject. The point of a haiku is implied rather than directly expressed. The writer — with a delicate and precise poetic "shorthand" — suggests the topic for meditation; the reader must draw his own conclusions and find his own messages. The search is a rewarding one.

Silent Flowers

Silent flowers
Speak also
To that obedient ear within.

Onitsura

I am one
Who eats his breakfast
Gazing at the morning-glories.

Basho

Stillness:
The sound of the petals
Sifting down together.

Chora

Sacred music at night;
Into the bonfires
Flutter the tinted leaves.

Issa

A day of rain;
Somebody passes my gate
With irises.

Shintoku

Round every house
The morning-glory blooms,
In the month of leaves.

Ryota

Just simply alive,
Both of us, I
And the poppy.

Issa

My eyes, having seen all,
Came back to
The white chrysanthemums.

Issho

The yellow chrysanthemums
Lose their color
In the light of the hand-lantern.

Buson

The scissors hesitate
Before the white chrysanthemums,
A moment.

Buson

The white chrysanthemums
Seem higher than they are,
In the morning twilight.

Yasen

A world of grief and pain:
Flowers bloom;
Even then .....

Issa

Overtaken by night among the blossoms,
I walk across the moor,
Home far distant.

Buson

To pluck it is a pity,
To leave it is a pity,
Ah, this violet!

Naojo

The short night;
The peony opened
During that time.

Buson

Hanging a lantern
On a blossoming bough,—
What pains I took!

Shiki

There is the moon;
And white and yellow crysanthemums;
Autumn draws to its close.

Shiki

They spoke no word.
The visitor, the host,
And the white chrysanthemum.

Ryota

From what flowering tree
I know not, —
But, ah, the fragrance!

Basho

Suddenly the sun rose,
To the scent of the plum-blossoms,
Along the mountain path.

Basho

Spreading a straw mat in the field,
I sat and gazed
At the plum blossoms.

Basho

In the moonlight,
The white plum-tree becomes again
A tree of winter.

Buson

The halo of the moon, —
Is it not the scent of plum-blossoms
Rising up to heaven?

Buson

Striking the fly,
I hit also
A flowering plant.

Issa

Simple trust:
Do not the petals flutter down,
Just like that?

Issa

A fallen flower
Returning to the branch?
It was a butterfly.

Moritake

How many, many things
They call to mind,
These cherry-blossoms!

Basho

Evening cherry-blossoms:
Today also now belongs
To the past.

Issa

When the peonies bloomed,
It seemed as though there were
No flowers around them.

Kiichi

"The peony was as big as this,"
Says the little girl,
Opening her arms.

Issa

The garden is dark
In the night, and quiet
The peony.

Shirao

After it was dark,
I began to want to change
The way I grafted it.

Issa

Sunrise — Moon-viewing

The first sunrise;
There is a cloud
Like a cloud in a picture.

Shusai

Sunbeams slant onto one side of the river;
From a floating cloud
Cold rain falls.

Kyoroku

A kite, —
In the same place
In yesterday's sky!

Buson

Oppressive heat;
My mind in a whirl
I listen to the peals of thunder.

Shiki

The thunderstorm having cleared up,
The evening sun shines on a tree
Where a cicada is chirping.

Shiki

I sit cooling beneath it,
Looking up
At the great tree.

Kyoroku

How long the day:
The boat is talking
With the shore.

Shiki

Billowing clouds;
White sails
Crowding in the south.

Shiki

Small islands are seen,
With the surf breaking round them,
In the haze.

Shoha

Fields and mountains
Drenched with rain, —
A cool day-break.

Shiki

All around
That meets the eye
Is cool and fresh.

Basho

How cool it is!
The clouds have great peaks,
And lesser peaks.

Issa

Desolately,
The sun sets in the rocks
On the withered moor.

Buson

The long night;
The sound of the water
Says what I think.

Gochiku

The night-light goes out;
The sound of the water:
The coolness.

Shiki

On an umbrella, a patter of raindrops,
But it enters next door;
The evening darkens.

Ranran

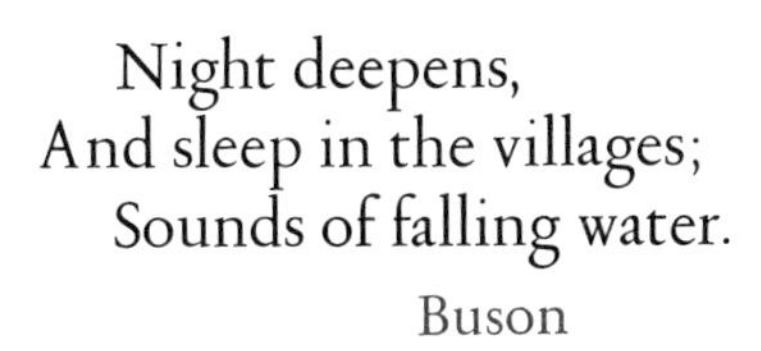

Night deepens,
And sleep in the villages;
Sounds of falling water.

Buson

Who is it that is awake,
The lamp still burning?
Cold rain at midnight.

Ryota

Moon-gazing:
Looking at it, it clouds over;
Not looking, it becomes clear.

Chora

The moon in the water;
Broken and broken again,
Still it is there.

Choshu

Tonight's moon! —
Unthinkable
That there was only one!

Ryota

The cool on the bridge;
The moon and I
Alone remain.

Kikusha-ni

The midnight moon, —
A ball
Of coolness?

Teishitsu

A handle
On the moon, —
And what a splendid fan!

Sokan

The moon in the water
Turned a somersault
And floated away.

Ryota

After the moon-viewing,
My shadow walking home
Along with me.

Sodo

In the Midst of the Plain . . .

In the midst of the plain
Sings the skylark,
Free of all things.

Basho

Out in the fields
Together with the birds,
I will be surrounded with mist.

Chora

Sneezing,
I lost sight
Of the skylark.

Yayu

The sparrows
Are playing hide-and-seek
Among the tea-flowers.

Issa

The stillness;
A bird walking on the fallen leaves:
The sound of it.

Ryushi

The butterfly is perfuming
Its wings, in the scent
Of the orchid.

Basho

The butterfly
Even when pursued,
Never appears in a hurry.

Garaku

The world
Is after all as the butterfly,
However it may be.

Soin

Distracted with the flowers,
Amazed at the moon,
The butterfly!

Chora

The butterfly having disappeared,
My spirit
Came back to me.

Wafu

The face of the dragon-fly
Is practically nothing
But eyes.

Chisoku

Reflected
In the eye of the dragon-fly
The distant hills.

Issa

Even the sound
Of the wings is heard, —
A cold, moon-lit night.

Seira

A cicada is chirping:
The toy wind-mill
Is bright red.

Issa

The silence!
The voice of the cicada
Penetrates the rocks.

Basho

Even among insects, in this world,
Some are good at singing,
Some bad.

Issa

The kitten
Holds down the leaf,
For a moment.

Issa

Being chased,
The fire-fly
Hides in the moon.

Ryota

You can see the morning breeze
Blowing the hairs
Of the caterpillar.

Buson

The swallow
Turns a somersault;
What has it forgotten?

Otsuyu

Grasshopper, —
Do not trample to pieces
The pearls of bright dew.

Issa

A shower came;
Running inside,
It cleared up.

Yuinen

The frog
Is having a staring-match
With me.

Issa

The old pond;
A frog jumps in, —
The sound of the water.

Basho

The frog
Rises up by the same force
With which it jumps in.

Torei

Oh, How Green . . .

Oh, how green
The threads of the willow,
Over the sliding waters!

Onitsura

Ah, how glorious!
The young leaves, the green leaves
Glittering in the sunshine!

Basho

A stream
Flowing through the town,
And the willows along it.

Shiki

Yield to the willow
All the loathing, all the desire
Of your heart.

Basho

In the cold sky of dawn
Only a single pine-tree
On the peak.

Gyodai

Dance from one blade of grass
To another,
Pearls of dew!

Ransetsu

The wind brings
Enough of fallen leaves
To make a fire.

Ryokan

A flash of lightning!
The sound of the dew
Dripping down the bamboos.

Buson

The grasses are misty,
The waters now silent;
It is evening.

Buson

The quietness;
A chestnut leaf sinks
Through the clear water.

Shohaku

A small garden
Brimming with dew,—
Half a gallon of it.

Shiki

Special Moments

Tranquillity:
Walking alone;
Happy alone.

Shiki

I walk over it alone,
In the cold moonlight:
The sound of the bridge.

Taigi

The stones at the bottom
Seem to be moving;
Clear water.

Soseki

Calm days,
The swift years
Forgotten.

Taigi

So happy to the eye,
The pure white fan
Of you whom I dearly love.

Buson

The first dream of the year;
I kept it a secret
And smiled to myself.

Sho-u

New Year's Day:
The desk and bits of paper, —
Just as last year.

Matsuo

Buying him a kite,
The child is fretful,
In the unending rain.

Shoha

The sound of tears
Hissing, quenching
The banked charcoal.

Basho

Slow days passing, accumulating,
How distant they are,
The things of the past!

Buson

How admirable,
He who thinks not, "Life is fleeting,"
When he sees the lightning!

Basho

The Seasons

Spring has come
In all simplicity:
A light yellow sky.

Issa

Yes, spring has come;
This morning a nameless hill
Is shrouded in mist.

Basho

Spring begins again;
Upon folly,
Folly returns.

Issa

Plum blossoms:
My spring
Is an ecstasy.

Issa

On the sandy beach,
Footprints:
Long is the spring day.

Shiki

It arose a perfect sphere, —
But how long it is,
This spring day!

Teitoku

A stray cat
Asleep on the roof
In the spring rain.

Taigi

Even my shadow
Is safe and sound and in the best of health
This first morning of spring.

Issa

In the water I draw up
Glitters the beginning
Of spring.

Ringai

Treading on the tail
Of the copper pheasant,
The setting sun of spring.

Buson

The beggar, —
He has heaven and earth
For his summer clothes!

Kikaku

Trees and stones,
Just as they are, —
The summer drawing-room.

Torin

Even the woodpecker
Will not harm this hermitage
Among the summer trees.

Basho

Summer in the world;
Floating on the waves
Of the lake.

Basho

What happiness,
Crossing this summer river,
Sandals in hand!

Buson

The summer moon
Is touched by the line
Of the fishing-rod.

Chiyo-ni

The summer moon;
On the other side of the river,
Who is it?

Chora

The sandy shore;
Why are they making a fire
Under the summer moon?

Shiki

Just the sound of it, —
But it was an evening
With a summer shower.

Issa

Should it have such worth,
What would I not give
For the scenery of autumn?

Soin

The beginning of autumn;
The sea and fields,
All one same green.

Basho

The mountain grows darker,
Taking the scarlet
From the autumn leaves.

Buson

Over the gold screen,
Whose silk gauze dress?
The autumn wind.

Buson

It is deep autumn:
My neighbor—
How does he live, I wonder?

Basho

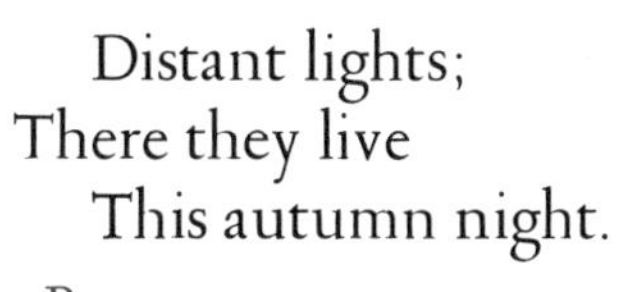

Distant lights;
There they live
This autumn night.

Buson

The autumn mountains;
Here and there
Smoke rising.

Gyodai

In a short life,
An hour of leisure,
This autumn evening.

Buson

Along this road
Goes no one,
This autumn eve.

Basho

An autumn eve;
There is a joy too,
In loneliness.

Buson

Winter

I surmise
From the shadow of the clothes-pole,
It is the depth of winter.

Shiki

The first snow,
Just enough to bend
The leaves of the daffodils.

Basho

Winter seclusion:
Once again I will lean against
This post.

Basho

This winter day,
It is warm in the sun, —
But cold!

Onitsura

I could eat it! —
This snow that falls
So softly, so softly.

Issa

Sweeping the garden,
The snow is forgotten
By the broom.

Basho

Fields and mountains, —
All taken by the snow;
Nothing remains.

Joso

There is neither heaven nor earth,
Only snow
Falling incessantly.

Hashin

Walking in the night;
Snow is falling,
A farewell to the year.

Shara

Under the winter moon,
The river wind
Sharpens the rocks.

Chora

KNUCKLE & POTTY DESTROY HAPPY WORLD

written and illustrated by

James Proimos

Christy Ottaviano Books
Henry Holt and Company New York

Henry Holt and Company, LLC, *Publishers since 1866*
175 Fifth Avenue, New York, New York 10010
mackids.com

Library of Congress Cataloging-in-Publication Data
Proimos, James.
Knuckle and Potty destroy Happy World / by James Proimos. — 1st ed.
p. cm.
Summary: When a place in a book called Happy World becomes
just too perfect and sweet for a tiger named Knuckle and a bear
named Potty, they decide the only way to get out is to erase it.
ISBN 978-0-8050-9155-7 (hc)
[1. Books—Fiction. 2. Tigers—Fiction. 3. Bears—Fiction.] I. Title.
PZ7.P9432Kn 2012 [Fic]—dc23 2011032002

Pen and ink and Corel Painter were used to
create the illustrations for this book.
First Edition—2012 / Designed by April Ward

Printed in China by Toppan Leefung Printing Ltd.,
Dongguan City, Guangdong Province

1 3 5 7 9 10 8 6 4 2

For Christy Ottaviano

KNUCKLE
& POTTY
DESTROY HAPPY WORLD
BOOM!
BOOM!

CHAPTER ONE

My name is Knuckle Tiggerelli. I became famous in the children's book *Tiger and Bear Are Huggable.* I'm the tiger. My good friend, Potty Polarberg, is the bear.

Farley Simpson, the guy who illustrated the book, drew us like so:

Humiliating, right?

Tiger and Bear Are Huggable has sold over a million copies to date.

Potty and I are also featured in the books *Tiger and Bear Are Cute*, *Tiger and Bear Are Sweet*, and *Tiger and Bear Are Wholesome*. Oh brother!

But it gets worse.

The author of these books, **Deli Cruz**, is halfway through her next book: *Tiger and Bear Go to Happy World.*

Potty and I are NOT CUTE!

WE ARE FED UP!

And there is no way we're going to Happy World!

But how do we get out of this Happy World book? Is it even possible? Are fictional characters like us powerless? Potty and I have no idea.

You may or may not realize that characters from books live in a special world somewhere between the author's brain and the printed word.

We decided to call on our friends who live in that space with us.

First stop, the beloved children's book character **Winkie the Pug**. He has been around forever. He'll know what to do.

WE NEED YOUR HELP, WINKIE.
BONE?
BONES
THE LADY WHO WRITES OUR BOOKS IS WORKING ON A NEW ONE THAT TAKES PLACE IN HAPPY WORLD!

AWESOME, DUDES!
CRUNCH
CRUNCH
NO, NOT AWESOME!
NOT AWESOME!
UNAWESOME.

Winkie the Pug explained that there was a way for us to go into the Outer World for five minutes at a time. We should use that time to talk to Deli Cruz and get her to change the next book.

But Winkie warned us that if we stayed in the Outer World for a

millisecond longer than the five minutes, we would cease to exist in both worlds.

The only other thing that could cause us to go kaput was a heartectomy. We didn't know what a heartectomy was, but we told him we didn't plan on having one.

Winkie said that all we had to do was **CLICK OUR HEELS** three times while **RUBBING OUR TUMMY** in a circular motion with one hand and **PATTING OUR HEAD** with the other.

We asked Winkie if he ever went into the Outer World. He told us he did once. He wanted more scenes in his book where he ate bonies. His author agreed if he promised never to go into the Outer World again.

That is how they get you, Winkie told us. Once you agree to that arrangement, the Outer World is off-limits **forever.**

CHAPTER TWO

Our author, Deli Cruz, is also a famous TV actress. She stars in the show *Those Talking Babies Are Mine*. The show is about baby brothers who talk with grown-up voices.

They say grown-up things, which is **funny** to people in the **Outer World**.

Deli Cruz plays their incredibly beautiful mom. She and the babies get into all kinds of

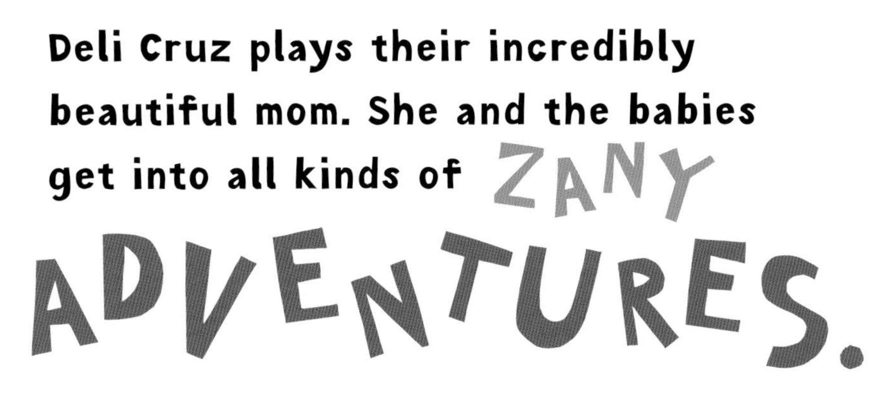

Here is a clip from the show:

YOU WANNA GET INTO SOME TROUBLE, BRO?
YOU KNOW I DO.
HOLD THAT THOUGHT. HERE COMES MOM.

DID YOU BOYS MOW THE LAWN AND WASH THE DOG LIKE I ASKED?
OOPS.
WE MAY HAVE MIXED THAT UP A TAD.

Then one of the babies says, "Well, at least the lawn is clean." Both babies smile real big into the camera, which gets a huge laugh.

Anyway, Potty read somewhere that Deli Cruz sits down to write every day at noon, and since it was noon, we attempted to click our heels, rub our tummies, and pat our heads. This was much harder to do than we thought it would be.

It took me forty-five minutes to master the task. But the second I did—POOF!—I entered the Outer World.

I WRITE THE TIGER AND BEAR BOOKS FOR HER.
SHE DOESN'T?
TOO BUSY!

GOOD GOLLY! YOU ARE TIGER! I WROTE YOU!
CALL ME KNUCKLE, AND COULD YOU PLEASE WRITE ME AS A TOUGH GUY?

HA! HA!
HA! HA!
HA!
HA!
HA!
HA!
HA!
HA!
HA!
HA!
TAP
TAP
UMPH!

I took a swat at the guy, missed, and fell off the desk. I started to cry a bit. Well, I had a little boo-boo from the fall. Even tough guys cry when they get boo-boos, don't they?

Now certain this so-called author would never write me as anything but cute, I licked my nose (oh yeah, that was the way Winkie the Pug told us we could return to our world) and—VOILA!—I was back home.

I landed right next to Potty who was still trying to master the tummy rubbing and head patting. I stopped him just before he figured it out.

I told Potty what had happened in the Outer World and asked him what we should do now. He said just one word: "CHICKEN."

Potty only speaks in one-word sentences. But he has a knack for making the one word really count. And so was the case in this instance.

CHAPTER THREE

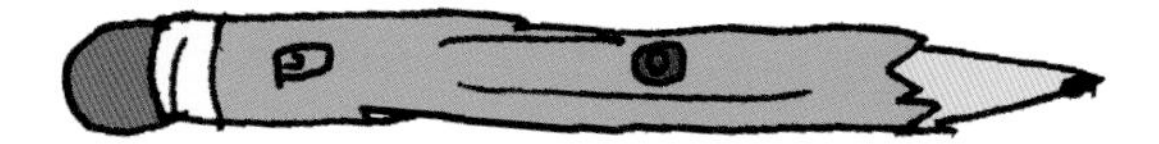

We went to see the Chicken. The Chicken in the Beret.

WE EXPLAINED OUR DILEMMA AND HE SAID THIS:
YOUR BEEF IS NOT WITH THE WRITER. IT'S WITH THE ARTIST.
YOU MUST GO TELL HIM TO DRAW YOU LESS WIMPY!
YES! LESS PINK, PERHAPS.

BUT DO NOT TELL HIM FROM UNDER THE SEA. DO NOT TELL HIM FROM UP IN A TREE. DO NOT TELL HIM FROM INSIDE A WHALE. DO NOT TELL HIM FROM INSIDE A JAIL.
DO NOT TELL HIM BY PERFORMING MIME. DO NOT TELL HIM IF IT'S PAST BEDTIME.
OKAY, WE GET IT.

The Chicken in the Beret was smart, but he went **ON** and **ON** about things even though you already got his point. He would just talk and talk even though you understood him. What I'm saying is that you would completely get what he was trying to tell you, but he would continue to repeat his message. He would keep explaining it. He would *say* it while sitting in a chair. He would *say* it in his underwear. He would *say* it while reading a book. He would *say* it while arresting a crook. He would *say* it while working out in a gym. He would *say* it—

Oh my gosh!

I am acting JUST LIKE HIM!

Sorry about that.

Back to the story. Potty and I need to see Farley Simpson, the artist who draws us. We must convince him to draw us as tough guys. My idea was to bring candy with us. If we brought some chocolate, I bet Farley would do whatever we asked. Chocolate is amazingly powerful. Even a whiff of it renders me powerless.

Potty's plan was to give the artist some good ideas about how to make us look **super cool**. He got out his art supplies and spent all day drawing. For your viewing pleasure, here are some of his sketches:

POTTY DREW ME WITH AN EYE PATCH.
POTTY DREW HIMSELF WITH A VILLAIN MUSTACHE.

POTTY DREW ME WITH FANGS.

POTTY DREW ME WITH BACK HAIR.

POTTY DREW HIMSELF WITH HORNS.
HE DREW ME IN A BUNNY SUIT...
BUT THAT WAS A BIG MISTAKE.

After reviewing Potty's drawings, I made the executive decision that chocolates were the way to go. I went to the fridge and got the heart-shaped box of chocolates I've been saving for my true love who I haven't met yet.

When Potty saw that I was taking the chocolates with us to the Outer World, he didn't say a word, but he let out a huge sigh. I could tell he was thinking, *But what happens if we meet your* ***true love****? What will you give* ***HER****?*

"Well, the only food in the fridge are three baby carrots that have been rolling around the bottom of the veggie drawer for the last two years. Perhaps those will do."

Potty shook his huge head back and forth.

"This is too important," I said. "Love will have to wait."

We immediately rubbed our tummies and patted our heads. In no time flat . . . we were standing in front of Farley Simpson.

CHAPTER FOUR

Farley was not surprised to see us. In fact, his very first words were,

On the other hand, Potty and I were very surprised because although he spoke in a much higher

voice, Farley Simpson looked exactly like the guy who wrote our books for Deli Cruz.

"He is my identical brother, Gregory Simpson," said Farley.

Then he stood up and got into a boxing stance.

DON'T ACT SO INNOCENT. MY BROTHER TOLD ME YOU TRIED TO CLOCK HIM.
I ASSURE YOU WE COME IN PEACE.

LOOK, WE EVEN BROUGHT YOU CHOCOLATES.

LEMME TRY ONE.
CERTAINLY.
MMMM.

Turns out Farley ate one of the very hot pepper-filled chocolates. Being an artist, he was especially sensitive to hot foods.

Needless to say, he refused to draw Potty and me as tough guys.

In fact, Farley was steaming mad. Or at the very least, just steaming.

I called the fire department and informed them we had a hothead on our hands.

When the fire trucks arrived, two guys jumped out and grabbed me. They put me on a stretcher, stuck a fire hose in my mouth, and turned it on **full blast**. I blew up like a GIANT WATER BALLOON.

After a brief struggle and a few minutes of deflation, I explained to them that I was always this color pink. The firefighters apologized, promised me I could ride on the hook and ladder in the near future, and attended to Farley.

With less than a minute to spare, we licked our noses and were home before we could say, "What the heck do we do now?"

And just as I was about to ask Potty that very question we were greeted by a familiar voice.

NOPE.

HOW ABOUT A DE-ZONKER?
!
?

CUCKOO.
ARE YOU CRAZY?
CRAZY LIKE A PUG.
WE ARE HERE TO GET YOU OUT OF THAT HAPPY BOOK.

Winkie the Pug explained that he and the Chicken in the Beret were having lunch the other day and decided that all Potty and I had to do was go into the book *Tiger and Bear Go to Happy World* and erase the place until kingdom comes.

"Erase the place?" I asked.

"Yep, all four of us go in there with really cool De-Zonkers and start erasing until all the happy is gone."

"Yes, De-Zonkers were featured in the book *Chicken in the Beret Comes Back Again*, and Chicken got to keep a closet full of them."

"That's all well and good," I said. "But those De-Zonkers look a little dangerous. How exactly do they work?"

BUT DO NOT ZONK IN A CROWD! DO NOT ZONK IF YOU DO NOT LIKE LOUD!
OH BOY.

DO NOT ZONK WHILE DRIVING A CAR! DO NOT ZONK IF YOU HAVE BEEN DRINKING FROM A JAR!

DO NOT ZONK
MY DOG
REX!
DO NOT
ZONK
WHILE YOU
TEXT!

DO NOT—
BOOM!
OOPS.
2

"Sorry, buddy," said Winkie the Pug. "You okay?"

The Chicken in the Beret nodded.

"Well, there's no time to waste.

LET'S GO, DUDES!"

yelled Winkie.

Chicken handed us each a De-Zonker.

Winkie handed us each a bicycle helmet and said, "Wear these for safety. They were extra designs from my book *Winkie the Pug Rides a Bike.*"

Even though they smelled like they'd been left in a musty cartoon basement for ages, we put them on.

"On the count of **three**, everyone rub your tummy and pat your head," said Winkie.

"One . . . two . . . three!"

NOW I SEE WHY YOU WANTED OUT OF THIS BOOK SO BADLY.
SO HAPPY, IT'S CREEPY.
YEESH!
!

CHAPTER FIVE

"Okay, here's the plan," said Winkie. "Potty, you take on the trees. Chicken, the flowers. I'll de-zonk the clouds. And, Knuckle, you get the bunny."

"What about the sun?" I asked.

"We leave the sun until last, because otherwise it will get dark, and I'm afraid of the dark."

"Me too," I said.

Potty and Chicken hugged each other for comfort at the very thought of darkness. I started to worry that the drawings in the book would sense our wimpiness, so I made a declaration:

"BESIDES THE DARK, WE'RE NOT AFRAID OF ANYTHING ELSE!"

"Wait a minute! What about **clowns**? Circus clowns, to be exact. I think we can all agree we're afraid of them," said Winkie.

"Shhhh," I whispered. "They can hear us." I bobbed my head toward the background.

It took Winkie a few seconds to understand what I was getting at.

"Oh, right! That was a funny joke, Knuckle! Us . . . afraid of clowns and the dark! Ha ha! **If anyone out there is listening, we are afraid of nothing!**" said Winkie in an extra-loud voice, making sure everyone on the page could hear him.

The clouds, flowers, trees, sun, and the rabbit all giggled in a cute way, and that annoyed us to no end.

"Let's **de-zonk** 'em, boys," said Winkie. "This should be a piece of cake."

THE FLOWERS TICKLED CHICKEN UNTIL HE FAINTED.
TICKLE.
TICKLE.
TICKLE.
GO TO SLEEP, GO TO SLEEP, GO TO SLEEP, LITTLE BABY...
ZZZZZZ
THE CLOUDS SANG A LULLABY THAT PUT WINKIE INTO A DEEP SLEEP.

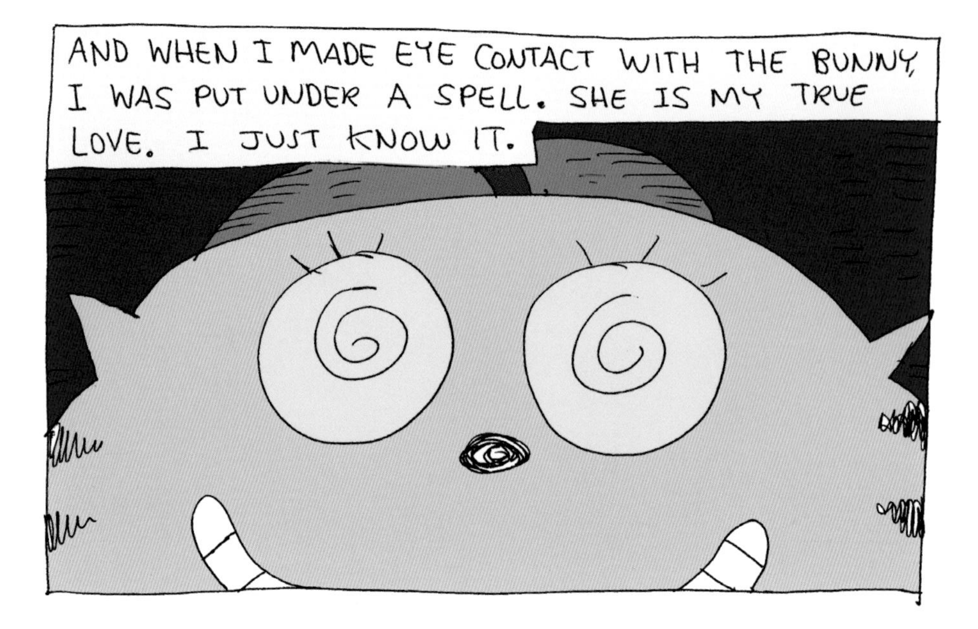

I don't know exactly what happened next because I left Happy World for a few minutes and went home for some essentials, but I'll get to that later.

What I'm told happened is the sun looked down on Potty, Winkie, and Chicken and chuckled.

"Welcome to Happy World, LOSERS!" shouted the sun.

Next, the sun sprouted three arms, reached down, and picked up each of our De-Zonkers.

"You don't come to Happy World and de-zonk us. **We de-zonk you!**" barked the sun.

Potty, Chicken, and Winkie were doomed!

ONE...
TWO...

AND JUST WHEN YOU WOULD THINK ALL WAS LOST, A HERO CAME ON THE SCENE WITH A SNAPPY LINE TO SAVE THE DAY.
NOT SO FAST, SUNNY BOY!
AND THAT SOMEONE WAS NOT ME (KNUCKLE).

IT WAS ACTUALLY THOSE OBNOXIOUS TWINS FROM THE TV SHOW THOSE TALKING BABIES ARE MINE!
ERASER
DROP THE DE-ZONKERS, OR WE START ERASING!

The sun dropped the De-Zonkers.

"Now order the clouds to start raining," said one of the babies.

The sun did. And the clouds rained. And the rain revived Potty, Winkie, and Chicken.

"KNUCKLE!" yelled Potty.

"Yipes! Where is Knuckle? We must find Knuckle!" said Winkie. "He must have de-zonked the bunny by now."

"The **bunny?**" said one cloud.

"Oh no," said the other cloud.

"That bunny is **super dangerous,**" said the sun.

POTTY WAS SO WORRIED ABOUT ME THAT HE TOOK MATTERS INTO HIS OWN HANDS.
BOOM!
YOU GOT HER.

The truth is I fell **madly** in **love** with Sarah at first sight. Sarah is the bunny.

I rushed back home to get Sarah the carrots from our fridge. She loved them.

Then I went back and put on the bunny costume Potty

had drawn for me. Sarah loved me even more.

Next thing you know, I am **de-zonkered** right through my middle. I got all dizzy and fell to the ground.

Potty and the others came running up to me.

"Oh no! Knuckle has been given a heartectomy!" said Winkie. "As I told you earlier, that's one of only two ways our kind can go KAPUT!"

Potty knelt down beside me and cradled my head in his hands. My eyes were closed but I could tell he was crying. I tried to make Potty feel better.

"You couldn't have got me in the heart, my friend," I whispered. "I just gave my heart to the bunny." But I was fading fast, and Potty knew it.

Suddenly, Potty got an idea. He took off his helmet. Inside were his art supplies.

He peeled me out of my rabbit suit and quickly **painted over** the hole in my center.

When he was done, not only did I feel great but I never looked better . . .

...OR TOUGHER.

It was a happy moment.

CHAPTER SIX

Winkie reminded us that we still needed to de-zonk everyone in Happy World.

But my near-kaput experience changed me. I got the clouds, sun, and trees together, and began making one of the greatest speeches ever given.

IS IT NOT BETTER TO LOVE THY BROTHER THAN TO DE-ZONK THY BROTHER? IS IT NOT BETTER TO PICK FLOWERS THAN FIGHTS?

IS IT NOT BETTER TO—
OOPS.
BOOM

Yes, they **de-zonked** my **kisser** mid-speech. But the important thing is that we all left Happy World as friends, with new mouths, courtesy of Potty.

We played Ping-Pong the rest of the day.

Took in a movie.

And over dinner at Eddie's Caramel Corn Hut, we decided we would write our next book ourselves.

And that book will be **ten times awesomer** than this one!

Although we may need to hire an

editor because we're not exactly sure *awesomer* is a word.

Tune in for our next adventure where we take on **comic book superheroes**.

The End